Keep a lasting record of how quickly your little VeggieTales® fan is growing!

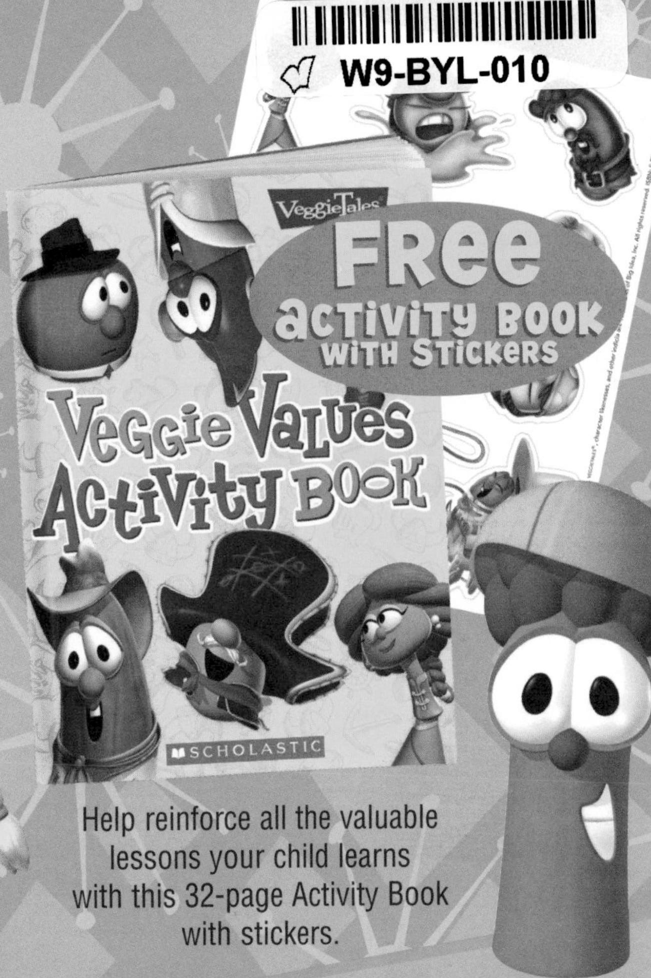

Help reinforce all the valuable lessons your child learns with this 32-page Activity Book with stickers.

2 BONUS BOOKS FOR THE PRICE OF 1

Just check the box on your order card to get these two jumbo-sized storybooks about being humble and forgiveness at 50% off – you get both for just $7.99.

PREVIEW THIS FUNNY TALE FREE FOR SEVEN DAYS!

Learn a lesson about making good choices when Cowboy Larry hits the trail! This hilarious book is yours for just $3.99 that's HALF OFF our everyday low price!

www.scholastic.com/drveggie **1-800-334-2515**

TURN HERE TO CLAIM ALL YOUR FREE BOOKS!

3 FREE HARDCOVER STORYBOOKS!
THREE PIRATES AND A DUCK
THE CASE OF THE LOST TEMPER
Good Knight, Duke
FREE ACTIVITY BOOK WITH STICKERS
Veggie Values Activity Book
FREE GROWTH CHART
☐ YES! Send my 3 FREE hardcover storybooks, FREE growth chart, FREE activity book with stickers, plus one more trial storybook for a FREE preview. If not delighted with my trial book, I'll return it at Scholastic's expense within seven days and owe nothing.
When I keep the trial book, I'll pay just $3.99 – that's HALF OFF the regular price – plus shipping and handling on the entire shipment, and become a member of the VeggieTales®: Values to Grow By program. I'll then receive two new values-filled storybooks and a new sheet of stickers about every four weeks for the everyday low price of $7.99 per book, plus shipping and handling. I may examine the books for seven days and return any I don't want at your expense. After purchasing as few as four shipments of two books each, I may cancel at any time by following the instructions on my invoice.
As a member of the VeggieTales: Values to Grow By book club who has purchased two club shipments, I will also automatically be enrolled in your separate Free Preview Program to receive, up to three times a year, seven-day free previews of special VeggieTales books or other VeggieTales items to supplement my club. You will always notify you first with details, price (usually between $15.00 to $20.00 plus shipping and handling), a reply form and a toll-free number. I'll tell you within 10 days if I choose not to receive a supplement, or do nothing and it will be sent. If you don't allow 10 days for my response, or if I don't want the selection, I may return it at your expense. Purchases made in the Free Preview Program do not count toward my membership agreement to purchase four regular club shipments. Club and Free Preview accounts must be canceled separately.
CODE: 875543WW3-9
☐ YES! Also send the 2 Bonus Books at 50% OFF!
Bill me an additional $7.99. If not satisfied, I'll return them within 7 days.
CODE: 875533WW3-0
Sales tax where applicable. Late charges apply to overdue payments. All orders subject to approval. Out-of-stock titles may be replaced by alternate selections.
Print Child's Full Name: ____ Birthdate: ____ (Month/Day/Year) ☐ Boy ☐ Girl
Print Your Full Name ☐ Mr. ☐ Mrs. ☐ Ms. ____
Address ____ Apt. ____
City ____ State ____ Zip ____
Telephone (____) ____ (Area Code)
E-mail (to confirm your order) ____
Have you bought anything by mail in the last: ☐ 6 months ☐ Year ☐ Never Do you own a computer? ☐ Yes ☐ No
TM & © Scholastic Inc. © 2007 Big Idea, Inc. VEGGIETALES®, character names, likenesses and other indicia are trademarks of Big Idea, Inc. All rights reserved. Used under license.
▲ DETACH HERE AND MAIL TODAY ▲
PLUS... CHECK THE BONUS BOOKS BOX TO GET THESE 2 BOOKS AT 50% OFF!
Hats Off to Lyle
LARRYBOY AND THE GOLDEN GUMBALLS
▼ DETACH HERE AND MAIL TODAY ▼
☐ YES! Send my 3 FREE hardcover storybooks, FREE growth chart, FREE activity book with stickers, plus one more trial storybook for a FREE preview. If not delighted with my trial book, I'll return it at Scholastic's expense within seven days and owe nothing.
When I keep the trial book, I'll pay just $3.99 – that's HALF OFF the regular price – plus shipping and handling on the entire shipment, and become a member of the VeggieTales®: Values to Grow By program. I'll then receive two new values-filled storybooks and a new sheet of stickers about every four weeks for the everyday low price of $7.99 per book, plus shipping and handling. I may examine the books for seven days and return any I don't want at your expense. After purchasing as few as four shipments of two books each, I may cancel at any time by following the instructions on my invoice.
As a member of the VeggieTales: Values to Grow By book club who has purchased two club shipments, I will also automatically be enrolled in your separate Free Preview Program to receive, up to three times a year, seven-day free previews of special VeggieTales books or other VeggieTales items to supplement my club. You will always notify you first with details, price (usually between $15.00 to $20.00 plus shipping and handling), a reply form and a toll-free number. I'll tell you within 10 days if I choose not to receive a supplement, or do nothing and it will be sent. If you don't allow 10 days for my response, or if I don't want the selection, I may return it at your expense. Purchases made in the Free Preview Program do not count toward my membership agreement to purchase four regular club shipments. Club and Free Preview accounts must be canceled separately.
CODE: 875543WW3-9
☐ YES! Also send the 2 Bonus Books at 50% OFF!
Bill me an additional $7.99. If not satisfied, I'll return them within 7 days.
CODE: 875533WW3-0
Sales tax where applicable. Late charges apply to overdue payments. All orders subject to approval. Out-of-stock titles may be replaced by alternate selections.
Print Child's Full Name: ____ Birthdate: ____ (Month/Day/Year) ☐ Boy ☐ Girl
Print Your Full Name ☐ Mr. ☐ Mrs. ☐ Ms. ____
Address ____ Apt. ____
City ____ State ____ Zip ____
Telephone (____) ____ (Area Code)
E-mail (to confirm your order) ____
Have you bought anything by mail in the last: ☐ 6 months ☐ Year ☐ Never Do you own a computer? ☐ Yes ☐ No
TM & © Scholastic Inc. © 2007 Big Idea, Inc. VEGGIETALES®, character names, likenesses and other indicia are trademarks of Big Idea, Inc. All rights reserved. Used under license.

NO POSTAGE NECESSARY IF MAILED IN THE UNITED STATES

BUSINESS REPLY MAIL

FIRST-CLASS MAIL PERMIT NO. 48 JEFFERSON CITY, MO

POSTAGE WILL BE PAID BY ADDRESSEE

SCHOLASTIC
PO BOX 6113
JEFFERSON CITY MO 65102-9669

▲ DETACH HERE AND MAIL TODAY ▲

Send Today for your 3 FREE BOOKS! FREE GROWTH CHART! FREE ACTIVITY BOOK WITH STICKERS!

NOTE: If all of the cards are missing, please write to:

VeggieTales: Values to Grow By
c/o Scholastic
P.O. Box 6038
Jefferson City, MO 65102-6038

For faster service:
order online at
www.scholastic.com/drveggie
or call us toll-free 1-800-334-2515

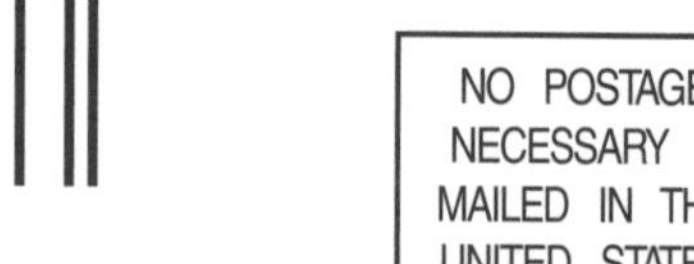

NO POSTAGE NECESSARY IF MAILED IN THE UNITED STATES

BUSINESS REPLY MAIL

FIRST-CLASS MAIL PERMIT NO. 48 JEFFERSON CITY, MO

POSTAGE WILL BE PAID BY ADDRESSEE

SCHOLASTIC
PO BOX 6113
JEFFERSON CITY MO 65102-9669

▲ DETACH HERE AND MAIL TODAY ▲

3 FREE HARDCOVER STORYBOOKS!
THREE PIRATES AND A DUCK
The Case of the LOST TEMPER
Good Knight, Duke
SCHOLASTIC
FREE ACTIVITY BOOK WITH STICKERS
Veggie Values Activity Book
SCHOLASTIC
VeggieTales
FREE GROWTH CHART
YES! SEND MY 3 FREE HARDCOVER STORYBOOKS, FREE GROWTH CHART, FREE ACTIVITY BOOK WITH STICKERS, PLUS ONE MORE TRIAL STORYBOOK FOR A FREE PREVIEW. If not delighted with my trial book, I'll return it at Scholastic's expense within seven days and owe nothing.
When I keep the trial book, I'll pay just $3.99 – that's HALF OFF the regular price – plus shipping and handling on the entire shipment, and become a member of the VeggieTales®: Values to Grow By program. I'll then receive two new values-filled storybooks and a new sheet of stickers about every four weeks for the everyday low price of $7.99 per book, plus shipping and handling. I may examine the books for seven days and return any I don't want at your expense. After purchasing as few as four shipments of two books each, I may cancel at any time by following the instructions on my invoice.
As a member of the VeggieTales: Values to Grow By book club who has purchased two club shipments, I will also automatically be enrolled in your separate Free Preview Program to receive, up to three times a year, seven-day free previews of special VeggieTales books or other VeggieTales items to supplement my club. You will always notify you first with details, price (usually between $15.00 to $20.00 plus shipping and handling), a reply form and a toll-free number. I'll tell you within 10 days if I choose not to receive a supplement, or do nothing and it will be sent. If you don't allow 10 days for my response, or if I don't want the selection, I may return it at your expense. Purchases made in the Free Preview Program do not count toward my membership agreement to purchase four regular club shipments. Club and Free Preview accounts must be canceled separately.
CODE: 875543WW3-9
YES! ALSO SEND THE 2 BONUS BOOKS AT 50% OFF!
Bill me an additional $7.99. If not satisfied, I'll return them within 7 days.
CODE: 875533WW3-0
Sales tax where applicable. Late charges apply to overdue payments. All orders subject to approval. Out-of-stock titles may be replaced by alternate selections.
Print Child's Full Name:
Birthdate: Month/Day/Year
Boy Girl
Print Your Full Name Mr. Mrs. Ms.
Address
Apt.
City
State
Zip
Telephone ( ) Area Code
E-mail (to confirm your order)
Have you bought anything by mail in the last: 6 months Year Never
Do you own a computer? Yes No
TM & © Scholastic Inc. © 2007 Big Idea, Inc. VEGGIETALES®, character names, likenesses and other indicia are trademarks of Big Idea, Inc. All rights reserved. Used under license.
▲ DETACH HERE AND MAIL TODAY ▲
PLUS... CHECK THE BONUS BOOKS BOX TO GET THESE 2 BOOKS AT 50% OFF!
Hats Off to Lyle
by Ronald Kidd
SCHOLASTIC
LARRYBOY AND THE GOLDEN GUMBALLS
SCHOLASTIC
▼ DETACH HERE AND MAIL TODAY ▼
YES! SEND MY 3 FREE HARDCOVER STORYBOOKS, FREE GROWTH CHART, FREE ACTIVITY BOOK WITH STICKERS, PLUS ONE MORE TRIAL STORYBOOK FOR A FREE PREVIEW. If not delighted with my trial book, I'll return it at Scholastic's expense within seven days and owe nothing.
When I keep the trial book, I'll pay just $3.99 – that's HALF OFF the regular price – plus shipping and handling on the entire shipment, and become a member of the VeggieTales®: Values to Grow By program. I'll then receive two new values-filled storybooks and a new sheet of stickers about every four weeks for the everyday low price of $7.99 per book, plus shipping and handling. I may examine the books for seven days and return any I don't want at your expense. After purchasing as few as four shipments of two books each, I may cancel at any time by following the instructions on my invoice.
As a member of the VeggieTales: Values to Grow By book club who has purchased two club shipments, I will also automatically be enrolled in your separate Free Preview Program to receive, up to three times a year, seven-day free previews of special VeggieTales books or other VeggieTales items to supplement my club. You will always notify you first with details, price (usually between $15.00 to $20.00 plus shipping and handling), a reply form and a toll-free number. I'll tell you within 10 days if I choose not to receive a supplement, or do nothing and it will be sent. If you don't allow 10 days for my response, or if I don't want the selection, I may return it at your expense. Purchases made in the Free Preview Program do not count toward my membership agreement to purchase four regular club shipments. Club and Free Preview accounts must be canceled separately.
CODE: 875543WW3-9
YES! ALSO SEND THE 2 BONUS BOOKS AT 50% OFF!
Bill me an additional $7.99. If not satisfied, I'll return them within 7 days.
CODE: 875533WW3-0
Sales tax where applicable. Late charges apply to overdue payments. All orders subject to approval. Out-of-stock titles may be replaced by alternate selections.
Print Child's Full Name:
Birthdate: Month/Day/Year
Boy Girl
Print Your Full Name Mr. Mrs. Ms.
Address
Apt.
City
State
Zip
Telephone ( ) Area Code
E-mail (to confirm your order)
Have you bought anything by mail in the last: 6 months Year Never
Do you own a computer? Yes No
TM & © Scholastic Inc. © 2007 Big Idea, Inc. VEGGIETALES®, character names, likenesses and other indicia are trademarks of Big Idea, Inc. All rights reserved. Used under license.

3 FREE HARDCOVER STORYBOOKS!
THREE PIRATES AND A DUCK
The Case of the LOST TEMPER
Good Knight, Duke
SCHOLASTIC
FREE ACTIVITY BOOK WITH STICKERS
Veggie Values Activity Book
VeggieTales
FREE GROWTH CHART
VeggieTales Values to Grow By
☐ YES! Send my 3 FREE hardcover storybooks, FREE Growth Chart, FREE activity Book with stickers, PLUS one more TRIAL storybook for a free preview. If not delighted with my trial book, I'll return it at Scholastic's expense within seven days and owe nothing.
When I keep the trial book, I'll pay just $3.99 – that's HALF OFF the regular price – plus shipping and handling on the entire shipment, and become a member of the VeggieTales®: Values to Grow By program. I'll then receive two new values-filled storybooks and a new sheet of stickers about every four weeks for the everyday low price of $7.99 per book, plus shipping and handling. I may examine the books for seven days and return any I don't want at your expense. After purchasing as few as four shipments of two books each, I may cancel at any time by following the instructions on my invoice.
As a member of the VeggieTales: Values to Grow By book club who has purchased two club shipments, I will also automatically be enrolled in your separate Free Preview Program to receive, up to three times a year, seven-day free previews of special VeggieTales books or other VeggieTales items to supplement my club. You will always notify you first with details, price (usually between $15.00 to $20.00 plus shipping and handling), a reply form and a toll-free number. I'll tell you within 10 days if I choose not to receive a supplement, or do nothing and it will be sent. If you don't allow 10 days for my response, or if I don't want the selection, I may return it at your expense. Purchases made in the Free Preview Program do not count toward my membership agreement to purchase four regular club shipments. Club and Free Preview accounts must be canceled separately.
CODE: 875543WW3-9
☐ YES! also send the 2 Bonus Books at 50% OFF!
Bill me an additional $7.99. If not satisfied, I'll return them within 7 days.
CODE: 875533WW3-0
Sales tax where applicable. Late charges apply to overdue payments. All orders subject to approval. Out-of-stock titles may be replaced by alternate selections.
Print Child's Full Name: ____ Birthdate: ____ Month/Day/Year ☐ Boy ☐ Girl
Print Your Full Name ☐ Mr. ☐ Mrs. ☐ Ms. ____
Address ____ Apt. ____
City ____ State ____ Zip ____
Telephone (____) ____ Area Code
E-mail (to confirm your order) ____
Have you bought anything by mail in the last: ☐ 6 months ☐ Year ☐ Never Do you own a computer? ☐ Yes ☐ No
TM & © Scholastic Inc. © 2007 Big Idea, Inc. VEGGIETALES®, character names, likenesses and other indicia are trademarks of Big Idea, Inc. All rights reserved. Used under license.
▲ DETACH HERE AND MAIL TODAY ▲
PLUS... CHECK THE BONUS BOOKS BOX TO GET THESE 2 BOOKS AT 50% OFF!
Hats Off to Lyle
LARRYBOY AND THE GOLDEN GUMBALLS
SCHOLASTIC
▼ DETACH HERE AND MAIL TODAY ▼
☐ YES! Send my 3 FREE hardcover storybooks, FREE Growth Chart, FREE activity Book with stickers, PLUS one more TRIAL storybook for a free preview. If not delighted with my trial book, I'll return it at Scholastic's expense within seven days and owe nothing.
When I keep the trial book, I'll pay just $3.99 – that's HALF OFF the regular price – plus shipping and handling on the entire shipment, and become a member of the VeggieTales®: Values to Grow By program. I'll then receive two new values-filled storybooks and a new sheet of stickers about every four weeks for the everyday low price of $7.99 per book, plus shipping and handling. I may examine the books for seven days and return any I don't want at your expense. After purchasing as few as four shipments of two books each, I may cancel at any time by following the instructions on my invoice.
As a member of the VeggieTales: Values to Grow By book club who has purchased two club shipments, I will also automatically be enrolled in your separate Free Preview Program to receive, up to three times a year, seven-day free previews of special VeggieTales books or other VeggieTales items to supplement my club. You will always notify you first with details, price (usually between $15.00 to $20.00 plus shipping and handling), a reply form and a toll-free number. I'll tell you within 10 days if I choose not to receive a supplement, or do nothing and it will be sent. If you don't allow 10 days for my response, or if I don't want the selection, I may return it at your expense. Purchases made in the Free Preview Program do not count toward my membership agreement to purchase four regular club shipments. Club and Free Preview accounts must be canceled separately.
CODE: 875543WW3-9
☐ YES! also send the 2 Bonus Books at 50% OFF!
Bill me an additional $7.99. If not satisfied, I'll return them within 7 days.
CODE: 875533WW3-0
Sales tax where applicable. Late charges apply to overdue payments. All orders subject to approval. Out-of-stock titles may be replaced by alternate selections.
Print Child's Full Name: ____ Birthdate: ____ Month/Day/Year ☐ Boy ☐ Girl
Print Your Full Name ☐ Mr. ☐ Mrs. ☐ Ms. ____
Address ____ Apt. ____
City ____ State ____ Zip ____
Telephone (____) ____ Area Code
E-mail (to confirm your order) ____
Have you bought anything by mail in the last: ☐ 6 months ☐ Year ☐ Never Do you own a computer? ☐ Yes ☐ No
TM & © Scholastic Inc. © 2007 Big Idea, Inc. VEGGIETALES®, character names, likenesses and other indicia are trademarks of Big Idea, Inc. All rights reserved. Used under license.

NO POSTAGE
NECESSARY IF
MAILED IN THE
UNITED STATES

BUSINESS REPLY MAIL
FIRST-CLASS MAIL PERMIT NO. 48 JEFFERSON CITY, MO

POSTAGE WILL BE PAID BY ADDRESSEE

SCHOLASTIC
PO BOX 6113
JEFFERSON CITY MO 65102-9669

◄ DETACH HERE AND MAIL TODAY ◄

Send Today for your
3 FREE BOOKS! FREE GROWTH CHART!
FREE ACTIVITY BOOK WITH STICKERS!

NOTE: IF ALL OF THE CARDS ARE MISSING, PLEASE WRITE TO:

VeggieTales: Values to Grow By
c/o Scholastic
P.O. Box 6038
Jefferson City, MO 65102-6038

For faster service:
order online at
www.scholastic.com/drveggie
or call us toll-free 1-800-334-2515

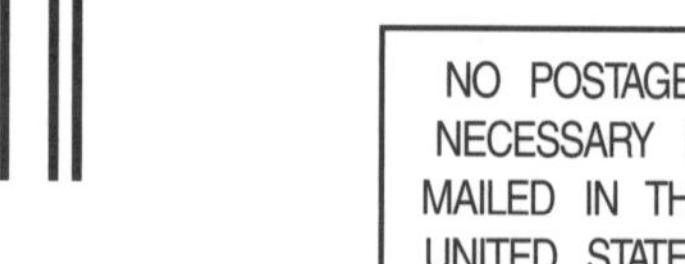

NO POSTAGE
NECESSARY IF
MAILED IN THE
UNITED STATES

BUSINESS REPLY MAIL
FIRST-CLASS MAIL PERMIT NO. 48 JEFFERSON CITY, MO

POSTAGE WILL BE PAID BY ADDRESSEE

SCHOLASTIC
PO BOX 6113
JEFFERSON CITY MO 65102-9669

◄ DETACH HERE AND MAIL TODAY ◄

3 FREE Hardcover Storybooks!
Three Pirates and a Duck
The Case of the Lost Temper
Good Knight, Duke
SCHOLASTIC
FREE Activity Book with Stickers
Veggie Values Activity Book
FREE Growth Chart
YES! Send my 3 FREE hardcover storybooks, FREE growth chart, FREE activity book with stickers, plus one more trial storybook for a FREE preview. If not delighted with my trial book, I'll return it at Scholastic's expense within seven days and owe nothing.
When I keep the trial book, I'll pay just $3.99 – that's HALF OFF the regular price – plus shipping and handling on the entire shipment, and become a member of the VeggieTales®: Values to Grow By program. I'll then receive two new values-filled storybooks and a new sheet of stickers about every four weeks for the everyday low price of $7.99 per book, plus shipping and handling. I may examine the books for seven days and return any I don't want at your expense. After purchasing as few as four shipments of two books each, I may cancel at any time by following the instructions on my invoice.
As a member of the VeggieTales: Values to Grow By book club who has purchased two club shipments, I will also automatically be enrolled in your separate Free Preview Program to receive, up to three times a year, seven-day free previews of special VeggieTales books or other VeggieTales items to supplement my club. You will always notify you first with details, price (usually between $15.00 to $20.00 plus shipping and handling), a reply form and a toll-free number. I'll tell you within 10 days if I choose not to receive a supplement, or do nothing and it will be sent. If you don't allow 10 days for my response, or if I don't want the selection, I may return it at your expense. Purchases made in the Free Preview Program do not count toward my membership agreement to purchase four regular club shipments. Club and Free Preview accounts must be canceled separately.
CODE: 875543WW3-9
YES! Also send the 2 Bonus Books at 50% OFF!
Bill me an additional $7.99. If not satisfied, I'll return them within 7 days.
CODE: 875533WW3-0
Sales tax where applicable. Late charges apply to overdue payments. All orders subject to approval. Out-of-stock titles may be replaced by alternate selections.
Print Child's Full Name: ______ Birthdate: ______ (Month/Day/Year) ☐ Boy ☐ Girl
Print Your Full Name ☐ Mr. ☐ Mrs. ☐ Ms. ______
Address ______ Apt. ______
City ______ State ______ Zip ______
Telephone (______) ______ (Area Code)
E-mail (to confirm your order) ______
Have you bought anything by mail in the last: ☐ 6 months ☐ Year ☐ Never Do you own a computer? ☐ Yes ☐ No
TM & © Scholastic Inc. © 2007 Big Idea, Inc. VEGGIETALES®, character names, likenesses and other indicia are trademarks of Big Idea, Inc. All rights reserved. Used under license.
▲ DETACH HERE AND MAIL TODAY ▲
PLUS... Check the Bonus Books Box to get these 2 books at 50% OFF!
Hats Off to Lyle
LarryBoy and the Golden Gumballs
▼ DETACH HERE AND MAIL TODAY ▼
YES! Send my 3 FREE hardcover storybooks, FREE growth chart, FREE activity book with stickers, plus one more trial storybook for a FREE preview. If not delighted with my trial book, I'll return it at Scholastic's expense within seven days and owe nothing.
When I keep the trial book, I'll pay just $3.99 – that's HALF OFF the regular price – plus shipping and handling on the entire shipment, and become a member of the VeggieTales®: Values to Grow By program. I'll then receive two new values-filled storybooks and a new sheet of stickers about every four weeks for the everyday low price of $7.99 per book, plus shipping and handling. I may examine the books for seven days and return any I don't want at your expense. After purchasing as few as four shipments of two books each, I may cancel at any time by following the instructions on my invoice.
As a member of the VeggieTales: Values to Grow By book club who has purchased two club shipments, I will also automatically be enrolled in your separate Free Preview Program to receive, up to three times a year, seven-day free previews of special VeggieTales books or other VeggieTales items to supplement my club. You will always notify you first with details, price (usually between $15.00 to $20.00 plus shipping and handling), a reply form and a toll-free number. I'll tell you within 10 days if I choose not to receive a supplement, or do nothing and it will be sent. If you don't allow 10 days for my response, or if I don't want the selection, I may return it at your expense. Purchases made in the Free Preview Program do not count toward my membership agreement to purchase four regular club shipments. Club and Free Preview accounts must be canceled separately.
CODE: 875543WW3-9
YES! Also send the 2 Bonus Books at 50% OFF!
Bill me an additional $7.99. If not satisfied, I'll return them within 7 days.
CODE: 875533WW3-0
Sales tax where applicable. Late charges apply to overdue payments. All orders subject to approval. Out-of-stock titles may be replaced by alternate selections.
Print Child's Full Name: ______ Birthdate: ______ (Month/Day/Year) ☐ Boy ☐ Girl
Print Your Full Name ☐ Mr. ☐ Mrs. ☐ Ms. ______
Address ______ Apt. ______
City ______ State ______ Zip ______
Telephone (______) ______ (Area Code)
E-mail (to confirm your order) ______
Have you bought anything by mail in the last: ☐ 6 months ☐ Year ☐ Never Do you own a computer? ☐ Yes ☐ No
TM & © Scholastic Inc. © 2007 Big Idea, Inc. VEGGIETALES®, character names, likenesses and other indicia are trademarks of Big Idea, Inc. All rights reserved. Used under license.

NO POSTAGE
NECESSARY IF
MAILED IN THE
UNITED STATES

BUSINESS REPLY MAIL
FIRST-CLASS MAIL PERMIT NO. 48 JEFFERSON CITY, MO

POSTAGE WILL BE PAID BY ADDRESSEE

SCHOLASTIC
PO BOX 6113
JEFFERSON CITY MO 65102-9669

▲ DETACH HERE AND MAIL TODAY ▲

Send Today for your
3 Free Books! Free Growth Chart!
Free Activity Book with Stickers!

Note: If all of the cards are missing, please write to:

VeggieTales: Values to Grow By
c/o Scholastic
P.O. Box 6038
Jefferson City, MO 65102-6038

For faster service:
order online at
www.scholastic.com/drveggie
or call us toll-free 1-800-334-2515

NO POSTAGE
NECESSARY IF
MAILED IN THE
UNITED STATES

BUSINESS REPLY MAIL
FIRST-CLASS MAIL PERMIT NO. 48 JEFFERSON CITY, MO

POSTAGE WILL BE PAID BY ADDRESSEE

SCHOLASTIC
PO BOX 6113
JEFFERSON CITY MO 65102-9669

☐ **YES! Send my 3 FREE hardcover storybooks, FREE growth chart, FREE activity book with stickers, plus one more trial storybook for a FREE preview.** If not delighted with my trial book, I'll return it at Scholastic's expense within seven days and owe nothing.

When I keep the trial book, I'll pay just $3.99 – that's HALF OFF the regular price – plus shipping and handling on the entire shipment, and become a member of the VeggieTales®: Values to Grow By program. I'll then receive two new values-filled storybooks and a new sheet of stickers about every four weeks for the everyday low price of $7.99 per book, plus shipping and handling. I may examine the books for seven days and return any I don't want at your expense. After purchasing as few as four shipments of two books each, I may cancel at any time by following the instructions on my invoice.

As a member of the VeggieTales: Values to Grow By book club who has purchased two club shipments, I will also automatically be enrolled in your separate Free Preview Program to receive, up to three times a year, seven-day free previews of special VeggieTales books or other VeggieTales items to supplement my club. You will always notify you first with details, price (usually between $15.00 to $20.00 plus shipping and handling), a reply form and a toll-free number. I'll tell you within 10 days if I choose not to receive a supplement, or do nothing and it will be sent. If you don't allow 10 days for my response, or if I don't want the selection, I may return it at your expense. Purchases made in the Free Preview Program do not count toward my membership agreement to purchase four regular club shipments. Club and Free Preview accounts must be canceled separately.

CODE: 875543WW3-9

☐ **YES! Also send the 2 Bonus Books at 50% OFF!** CODE: 875533WW3-0
Bill me an additional $7.99. If not satisfied, I'll return them within 7 days.

Sales tax where applicable. Late charges apply to overdue payments. All orders subject to approval. Out-of-stock titles may be replaced by alternate selections.

Print Child's Full Name: ______ Birthdate: ______ (Month/Day/Year) ☐ Boy ☐ Girl

Print Your Full Name ☐ Mr. ☐ Mrs. ☐ Ms. ______

Address ______ Apt. ______

City ______ State ______ Zip ______

Telephone (______ Area Code) ______

E-mail (to confirm your order) ______

Have you bought anything by mail in the last: ☐ 6 months ☐ Year ☐ Never Do you own a computer? ☐ Yes ☐ No

☐ **YES! Send my 3 FREE hardcover storybooks, FREE growth chart, FREE activity book with stickers, plus one more trial storybook for a FREE preview.** If not delighted with my trial book, I'll return it at Scholastic's expense within seven days and owe nothing.

When I keep the trial book, I'll pay just $3.99 – that's HALF OFF the regular price – plus shipping and handling on the entire shipment, and become a member of the VeggieTales®: Values to Grow By program. I'll then receive two new values-filled storybooks and a new sheet of stickers about every four weeks for the everyday low price of $7.99 per book, plus shipping and handling. I may examine the books for seven days and return any I don't want at your expense. After purchasing as few as four shipments of two books each, I may cancel at any time by following the instructions on my invoice.

As a member of the VeggieTales: Values to Grow By book club who has purchased two club shipments, I will also automatically be enrolled in your separate Free Preview Program to receive, up to three times a year, seven-day free previews of special VeggieTales books or other VeggieTales items to supplement my club. You will always notify you first with details, price (usually between $15.00 to $20.00 plus shipping and handling), a reply form and a toll-free number. I'll tell you within 10 days if I choose not to receive a supplement, or do nothing and it will be sent. If you don't allow 10 days for my response, or if I don't want the selection, I may return it at your expense. Purchases made in the Free Preview Program do not count toward my membership agreement to purchase four regular club shipments. Club and Free Preview accounts must be canceled separately.

CODE: 875543WW3-9

☐ **YES! Also send the 2 Bonus Books at 50% OFF!** CODE: 875533WW3-0
Bill me an additional $7.99. If not satisfied, I'll return them within 7 days.

Sales tax where applicable. Late charges apply to overdue payments. All orders subject to approval. Out-of-stock titles may be replaced by alternate selections.

Print Child's Full Name: ______ Birthdate: ______ (Month/Day/Year) ☐ Boy ☐ Girl

Print Your Full Name ☐ Mr. ☐ Mrs. ☐ Ms. ______

Address ______ Apt. ______

City ______ State ______ Zip ______

Telephone (______ Area Code) ______

E-mail (to confirm your order) ______

Have you bought anything by mail in the last: ☐ 6 months ☐ Year ☐ Never Do you own a computer? ☐ Yes ☐ No

TM & © Scholastic Inc. © 2007 Big Idea, Inc. VEGGIETALES®, character names, likenesses and other indicia are trademarks of Big Idea, Inc. All rights reserved. Used under license.

NO POSTAGE NECESSARY IF MAILED IN THE UNITED STATES

BUSINESS REPLY MAIL
FIRST-CLASS MAIL PERMIT NO. 48 JEFFERSON CITY, MO

POSTAGE WILL BE PAID BY ADDRESSEE

SCHOLASTIC
PO BOX 6113
JEFFERSON CITY MO 65102-9669

▲ DETACH HERE AND MAIL TODAY ▲

Send Today for your
3 FREE BOOKS! FREE GROWTH CHART!
FREE ACTIVITY BOOK WITH STICKERS!

NOTE: IF ALL OF THE CARDS ARE MISSING, PLEASE WRITE TO:

VeggieTales: Values to Grow By
c/o Scholastic
P.O. Box 6038
Jefferson City, MO 65102-6038

For faster service:
order online at
www.scholastic.com/drveggie
or call us toll-free 1-800-334-2515

NO POSTAGE NECESSARY IF MAILED IN THE UNITED STATES

BUSINESS REPLY MAIL
FIRST-CLASS MAIL PERMIT NO. 48 JEFFERSON CITY, MO

POSTAGE WILL BE PAID BY ADDRESSEE

SCHOLASTIC
PO BOX 6113
JEFFERSON CITY MO 65102-9669

▲ DETACH HERE AND MAIL TODAY ▲

3 FREE HARDCOVER STORYBOOKS!
THREE PIRATES AND A DUCK
The Case of the LOST TEMPER
Good Knight, Duke
SCHOLASTIC
FREE ACTIVITY BOOK WITH STICKERS
VeggieTales
Veggie Values Activity Book
SCHOLASTIC
VeggieTales
Values to Grow By
FREE GROWTH CHART
YES! Send my 3 FREE hardcover storybooks, FREE Growth Chart, FREE Activity Book with Stickers, plus one more trial storybook for a FREE preview. If not delighted with my trial book, I'll return it at Scholastic's expense within seven days and owe nothing.
When I keep the trial book, I'll pay just $3.99 – that's HALF OFF the regular price – plus shipping and handling on the entire shipment, and become a member of the VeggieTales®: Values to Grow By program. I'll then receive two new values-filled storybooks and a new sheet of stickers about every four weeks for the everyday low price of $7.99 per book, plus shipping and handling. I may examine the books for seven days and return any I don't want at your expense. After purchasing as few as four shipments of two books each, I may cancel at any time by following the instructions on my invoice.
As a member of the VeggieTales: Values to Grow By book club who has purchased two club shipments, I will also automatically be enrolled in your separate Free Preview Program to receive, up to three times a year, seven-day free previews of special VeggieTales books or other VeggieTales items to supplement my club. You will always notify you first with details, price (usually between $15.00 to $20.00 plus shipping and handling), a reply form and a toll-free number. I'll tell you within 10 days if I choose not to receive a supplement, or do nothing and it will be sent. If you don't allow 10 days for my response, or if I don't want the selection, I may return it at your expense. Purchases made in the Free Preview Program do not count toward my membership agreement to purchase four regular club shipments. Club and Free Preview accounts must be canceled separately.
CODE: 875543WW3-9
YES! Also send the 2 Bonus Books at 50% OFF!
Bill me an additional $7.99. If not satisfied, I'll return them within 7 days.
CODE: 875533WW3-0
Sales tax where applicable. Late charges apply to overdue payments. All orders subject to approval. Out-of-stock titles may be replaced by alternate selections.
Print Child's Full Name: Birthdate: Month/Day/Year ☐ Boy ☐ Girl
Print Your Full Name ☐ Mr. ☐ Mrs. ☐ Ms.
Address Apt.
City State Zip
Telephone ( ) Area Code
E-mail (to confirm your order)
Have you bought anything by mail in the last: ☐ 6 months ☐ Year ☐ Never Do you own a computer? ☐ Yes ☐ No
TM & © Scholastic Inc. © 2007 Big Idea, Inc. VEGGIETALES®, character names, likenesses and other indicia are trademarks of Big Idea, Inc. All rights reserved. Used under license.
▲ DETACH HERE AND MAIL TODAY ▲
PLUS... CHECK THE BONUS BOOKS BOX TO GET THESE 2 BOOKS AT 50% OFF!
Hats Off to Lyle
LARRYBOY AND THE GOLDEN GUMBALLS
SCHOLASTIC
▼ DETACH HERE AND MAIL TODAY ▼
YES! Send my 3 FREE hardcover storybooks, FREE Growth Chart, FREE Activity Book with Stickers, plus one more trial storybook for a FREE preview. If not delighted with my trial book, I'll return it at Scholastic's expense within seven days and owe nothing.
When I keep the trial book, I'll pay just $3.99 – that's HALF OFF the regular price – plus shipping and handling on the entire shipment, and become a member of the VeggieTales®: Values to Grow By program. I'll then receive two new values-filled storybooks and a new sheet of stickers about every four weeks for the everyday low price of $7.99 per book, plus shipping and handling. I may examine the books for seven days and return any I don't want at your expense. After purchasing as few as four shipments of two books each, I may cancel at any time by following the instructions on my invoice.
As a member of the VeggieTales: Values to Grow By book club who has purchased two club shipments, I will also automatically be enrolled in your separate Free Preview Program to receive, up to three times a year, seven-day free previews of special VeggieTales books or other VeggieTales items to supplement my club. You will always notify you first with details, price (usually between $15.00 to $20.00 plus shipping and handling), a reply form and a toll-free number. I'll tell you within 10 days if I choose not to receive a supplement, or do nothing and it will be sent. If you don't allow 10 days for my response, or if I don't want the selection, I may return it at your expense. Purchases made in the Free Preview Program do not count toward my membership agreement to purchase four regular club shipments. Club and Free Preview accounts must be canceled separately.
CODE: 875543WW3-9
YES! Also send the 2 Bonus Books at 50% OFF!
Bill me an additional $7.99. If not satisfied, I'll return them within 7 days.
CODE: 875533WW3-0
Sales tax where applicable. Late charges apply to overdue payments. All orders subject to approval. Out-of-stock titles may be replaced by alternate selections.
Print Child's Full Name: Birthdate: Month/Day/Year ☐ Boy ☐ Girl
Print Your Full Name ☐ Mr. ☐ Mrs. ☐ Ms.
Address Apt.
City State Zip
Telephone ( ) Area Code
E-mail (to confirm your order)
Have you bought anything by mail in the last: ☐ 6 months ☐ Year ☐ Never Do you own a computer? ☐ Yes ☐ No
TM & © Scholastic Inc. © 2007 Big Idea, Inc. VEGGIETALES®, character names, likenesses and other indicia are trademarks of Big Idea, Inc. All rights reserved. Used under license.

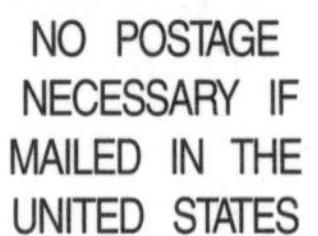

NO POSTAGE NECESSARY IF MAILED IN THE UNITED STATES

BUSINESS REPLY MAIL

FIRST-CLASS MAIL PERMIT NO. 48 JEFFERSON CITY, MO

POSTAGE WILL BE PAID BY ADDRESSEE

SCHOLASTIC
PO BOX 6113
JEFFERSON CITY MO 65102-9669

▲ DETACH HERE AND MAIL TODAY ▲

Send Today for your

3 FREE BOOKS! FREE GROWTH CHART! FREE ACTIVITY BOOK WITH STICKERS!

NOTE: IF ALL OF THE CARDS ARE MISSING, PLEASE WRITE TO:

VeggieTales: Values to Grow By
c/o Scholastic
P.O. Box 6038
Jefferson City, MO 65102-6038

For faster service:
order online at
www.scholastic.com/drveggie
or call us toll-free 1-800-334-2515

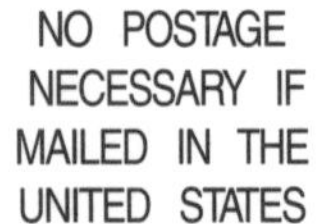

NO POSTAGE NECESSARY IF MAILED IN THE UNITED STATES

BUSINESS REPLY MAIL

FIRST-CLASS MAIL PERMIT NO. 48 JEFFERSON CITY, MO

POSTAGE WILL BE PAID BY ADDRESSEE

SCHOLASTIC
PO BOX 6113
JEFFERSON CITY MO 65102-9669

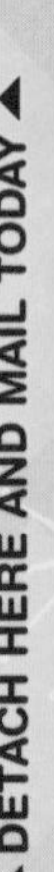

▲ DETACH HERE AND MAIL TODAY ▲

SCHOLASTIC
P.O. BOX 6038, JEFFERSON CITY, MO 65102-6038
www.HomeClubs.Scholastic.com

Dear Parent,

We want to send you these three FREE *VeggieTales: Values to Grow By* storybooks to encourage your child's love of reading.

As the most trusted name in learning today, we know just what that takes! Scholastic's books have been used by thousands of teachers across the country to teach millions of children to read. We're the #1 resource for parents like you for the widest variety of innovative products that help children learn at home.

Parents turn to us to find just the right products for their children's specific needs and interests. From programs to enrich their children's skills … sensible solutions to pressing concerns … homework help, research projects, reading tips and more.

After all, we're parents, too! And, speaking as a mom, these *VeggieTales: Values to Grow By* storybooks make story time one of the best times my family shares. My kids love the comical adventures starring the VeggieTales friends. I love the way that each storybook shares a positive message about values – from being nice and being responsible, to showing faith and showing mercy. These are delightful stories (with valuable lessons!) that are sure to be read again and again.

So, enjoy this book with your child right now. Then fill out and mail one of the order cards at left and watch your child start learning … and loving every minute of it!

Sincerely,

Mary-Alice Moore

Mary-Alice Moore
Editorial Director
(and mother of three!)

NOTE: If all of the cards are missing, please write to:
VeggieTales: Values to Grow By, c/o Scholastic, P.O. Box 6038, Jefferson City, MO 65102-6038

This book belongs to

Published by Scholastic Inc., 90 Old Sherman Turnpike, Danbury, Connecticut 06816.

ISBN: 0-7172-9926-0

Printed in the U.S.A.

First Scholastic printing, April 2006

THE GOOD, THE BAD, AND THE SILLY

A Lesson in *Making Good Choices*

by
Doug Peterson

Illustrated by
Tom Bancroft
and Rob Corley
Colored by Jon Conkling

SCHOLASTIC INC.
New York Toronto London Auckland Sydney
Mexico City New Delhi Hong Kong Buenos Aires

I
EAU
TFQI
RYNOM
HOW TO
PARALLEL
PARK
a
STAGECOACH

Bong! The clock struck high noon.

Cowboy Larry was shakin' in his boots—it was the day of his big cattle-drive test at Cowboy School.

Sheriff Bob, the cattle-drive teacher, glanced at the names on his clipboard. "Next up: Cowboy Larry, Botch Scallion, and the Sunburn Kid," he said.

Cowboy Larry's heart pounded like a hammer. It was his turn!

In this test, Cowboy Larry would have to move 40 cows from one ranch to another. If he could do it fast enough, he would pass with flying colors. But he would have to work as part of a team. And his partners would be none other than those rascals Botch Scallion and the Sunburn Kid.

"Howdy, partners," Cowboy Larry said to Botch and Sunburn.

Botch snarled, as crabby as a cowpoke with a cactus in his pants. But the Sunburn Kid didn't answer at all. He was too busy trying to cover his belly with sunscreen.

Splurt! The sunscreen splattered Cowboy Larry in the nose instead. "Oops—sorry!" said the Sunburn Kid.

Cowboy Larry ***really*** wanted to pass the cattle-drive test. After all, he didn't do very well on his advanced-moseying test the week before.

"You know how it works, boys," said Bob. "You've got to move those cows from the Okie-Dokie Corral and around Dodge Ball Canyon. Get the cows to the Ranch Dressing Ranch before sundown and you pass."

"Sounds good. Let's round 'em up!" shouted Cowboy Larry, but Botch just growled. The Sunburn Kid didn't say a word, because he was too busy putting T-shirts on the cows—to keep the sun off their backs.

The cattle-drive test started out wonderfully. Cowboy Larry rode alongside the cows, shouting cowboy things like "Rollin', rollin', rollin', keep them doggies moving!"—even though they were cows and not dogs.

But as they neared Dodge Ball Canyon, Botch led the cattle off the trail. He took the cows down into the canyon.

"Uh . . . Mr. Botch, aren't we supposed to take the cows **around** Dodge Ball Canyon?" asked Cowboy Larry.

"This is the shortcut," muttered Botch.

"But cutting through Dodge Ball Canyon would be cheating," said Cowboy Larry.

"So what? You got a problem, boy?"

"Well . . . yeah," Cowboy Larry said. "God has a problem with it, too."

"But cheating gets good grades," said Botch. "Isn't that true, Sunburn?"

The Sunburn Kid didn't answer.

Cowboy Larry knew that taking a shortcut through Dodge Ball Canyon wouldn't just be cheating—it would be dangerous. Mountain lions prowled the canyon. And if they made too much noise, they could trigger a deadly avalanche of dodge balls.

"Are you coming or not?" asked Botch.

Cowboy Larry wasn't sure what to do. Should he do the **good** thing and say he won't go along with the others? Should he do the **bad** thing and follow Botch and the Sunburn Kid? Or should he do the **silly** thing and help Sunburn put hats and sunglasses on all the cows to protect their eyes from dangerous ultraviolet rays?

"C'mon," snarled Botch. "Who's even gonna know we cheated?"

"Well . . . okay," said Cowboy Larry. He decided to follow Botch and the Sunburn Kid, but Cowboy Larry felt rotten about it.

So they led the cows into the deadly Dodge Ball Canyon. Buzzards circled overhead. Lizards lay out in the sun. Tumbleweeds blew by. And the Sunburn Kid nearly got bit trying to put sunscreen on rattlesnakes.

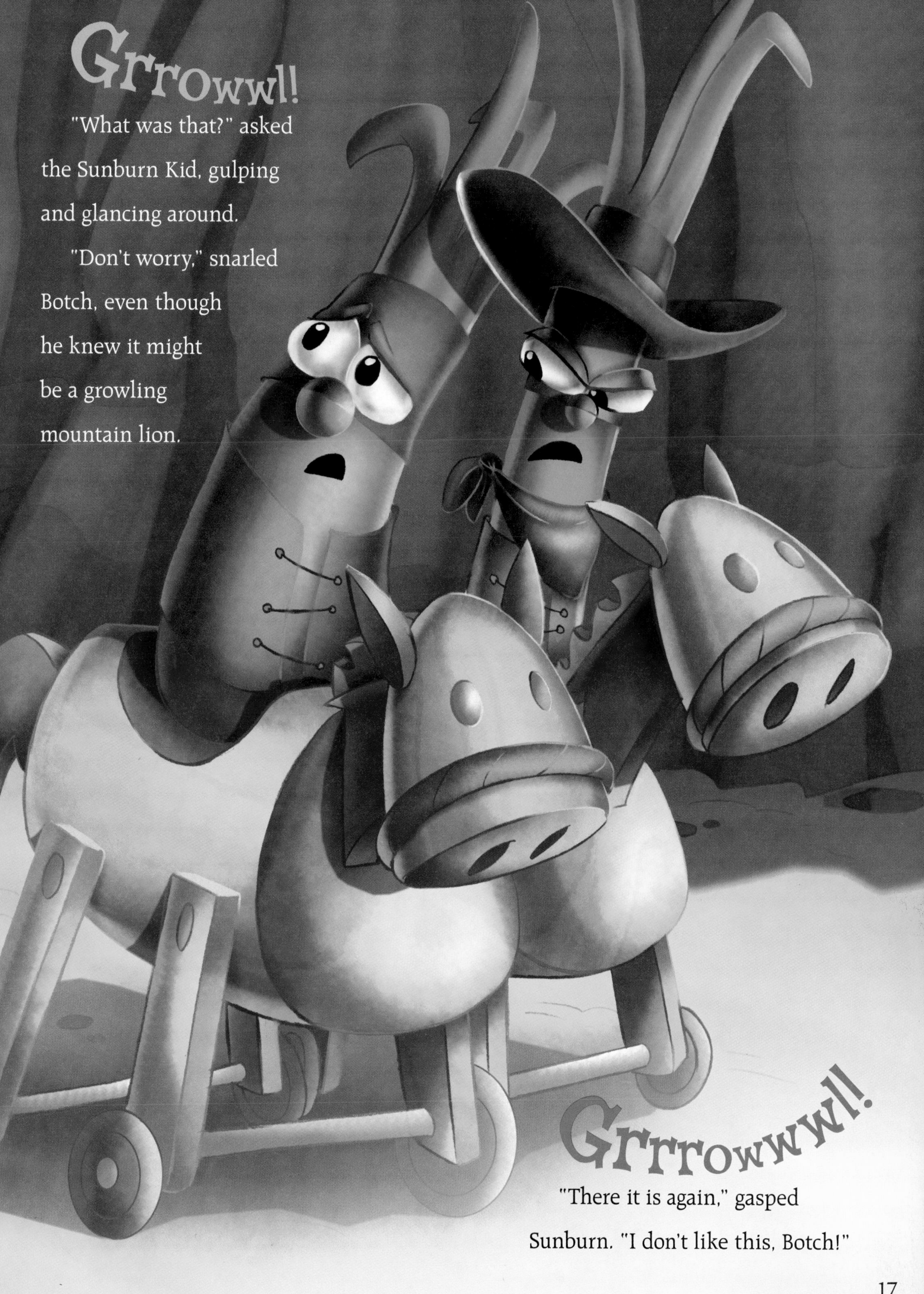

Grrowwl!

"What was that?" asked the Sunburn Kid, gulping and glancing around.

"Don't worry," snarled Botch, even though he knew it might be a growling mountain lion.

Grrrowwwl!

"There it is again," gasped Sunburn. "I don't like this, Botch!"

By this time, Cowboy Larry knew he had made the wrong choice. He shouldn't have decided to cheat. But he also realized that it wasn't too late to change his mind.

It's never too late to do the **good** thing.

"You asked who's going to know if we cheat," Cowboy Larry said to Botch. "Well . . . ***I'll*** know. And so will God. So I'm turning around. Are you coming or not?"

"Good riddance," grumbled Botch. **"Adiós, amigo."**

But as Cowboy Larry rode out of Dodge Ball Canyon, Botch and the Sunburn Kid suddenly heard it again.

Grrrrrowwwwwl!

Botch rolled his eyes. "That isn't a mountain lion growling," he said to Sunburn. "That's your ***stomach*** growling."

"Gee, I think you're right," said Sunburn. "I knew I should've ordered ***three*** flapjack breakfasts this morning at Clint's Covered Wagon Café."

Cows are not especially smart. The more they heard Sunburn's stomach growling, the more afraid they became. They were sure it was the sound of growling mountain lions.

Finally, one of the cows couldn't take it any longer. Terrified, she ran! And when one cow bolted, all of them did.

"Stampede!" shouted Botch.

Wildly out of control, the cattle thundered across the land, kicking up dust. They shook the ground like an earthquake. The result?

"Avalanche!" exclaimed the Sunburn Kid.

Thousands of dodge balls came crashing down from the hills, burying the cowboys in bouncy rubber balls.

Cowboy Larry got out of the canyon just before the avalanche happened. When the dust settled, he was able to gallop back and throw a rope to Botch and Sunburn. He pulled them and the cows out from under the dodge balls.

Yippie Ki Yea, Ki Yea! Cowboy Larry had saved the day!

"Good thing I didn't stay with you guys," he told Botch and Sunburn. Cowboy Larry had learned to follow God, rather than follow the crowd—or the herd.

It was dark by the time they returned to the Okie-Dokie Corral. Miss Kitty, the Cowboy School owner, handed root beers to the tired cowboys.

"I'm sorry," said Sheriff Bob. "I can't give you your Cattle-Drive License today."

Cowboy Larry was as happy as could be. Although he didn't pass the cattle-drive test, he had passed a more important test. He didn't cheat.

Cowboy Larry had made the **good** choice after all.

The Sunburn Kid, meanwhile, didn't mind that they had failed. Night had fallen in the Wild, Wild West, and he was too busy smearing "moonscreen" on his face.

Splurt!

"Oops—sorry!" he said to Cowboy Larry.

Do not follow the crowd when they do what is wrong.
Exodus 23:2